Contents

Welcome! 3

Unit 1: Weather 7

Unit 2: Journeys 12

Unit 3: Fox at the Farm 17

Unit 4: Fun at the Fair 22

Unit 5: At the Castle 27

Unit 6: A Camping Trip 32

Unit 7: Doctor, Doctor! 37

Unit 8: A Party 42

Certificate 47

Welcome!

Track 1 Track 2

Welcome Unit, Lesson 1: Chant

Track 3 Track 4

Welcome Unit, Lesson 2: Vocabulary

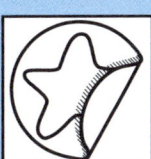

Weather

Unit 1, Lesson 1: Vocabulary

Review 1: /w/, /ng/

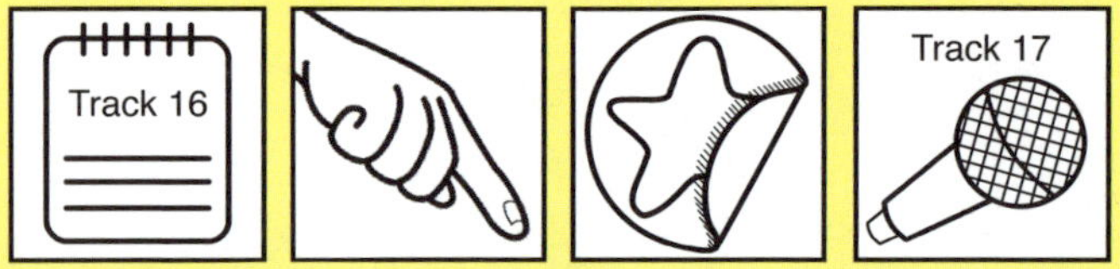

 Track 16

 Track 17

Journeys

Unit 2, Lesson 1: Vocabulary

Track 19

Unit 2, Lesson 3: Story

Review 2: /v/, /oo/, /oo/

Fox at the Farm

Unit 3, Lesson 1: Vocabulary

Review 3: /y/, /x/, /ch/

Fun at the Fair

Unit 4, Lesson 1: Vocabulary

Track 34

Review 4: /sh/, /th/, /th/

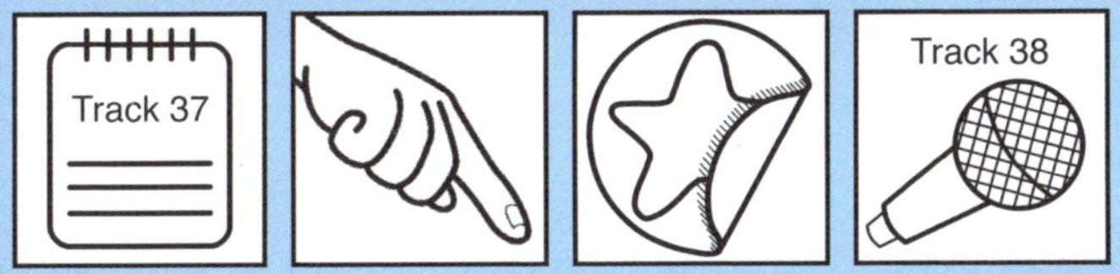

 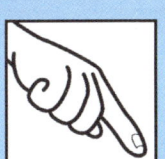  

At the Castle

Unit 5, Lesson 1: Vocabulary

Unit 5, Lesson 2: Vocabulary

Review 5: /qu/, /ou/, /oi/

A Camping Trip

Unit 6, Lesson 1: Vocabulary

Track 47 Track 48

Unit 6, Lesson 2: Vocabulary

Track 49

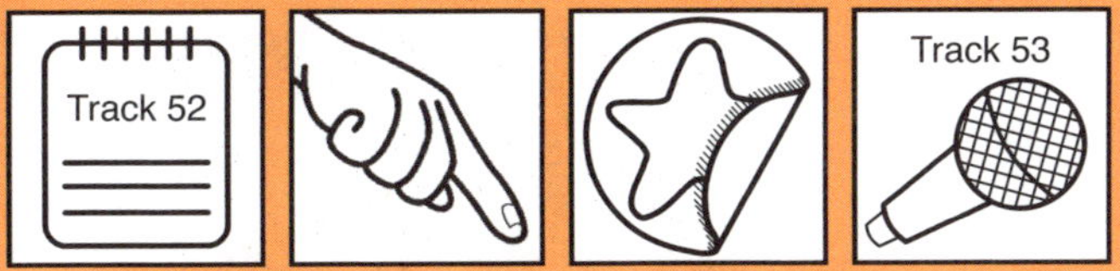

    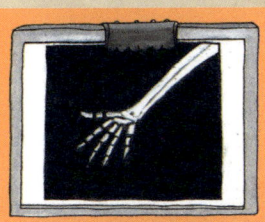

Doctor, Doctor!

Unit 7, Lesson 1: Vocabulary

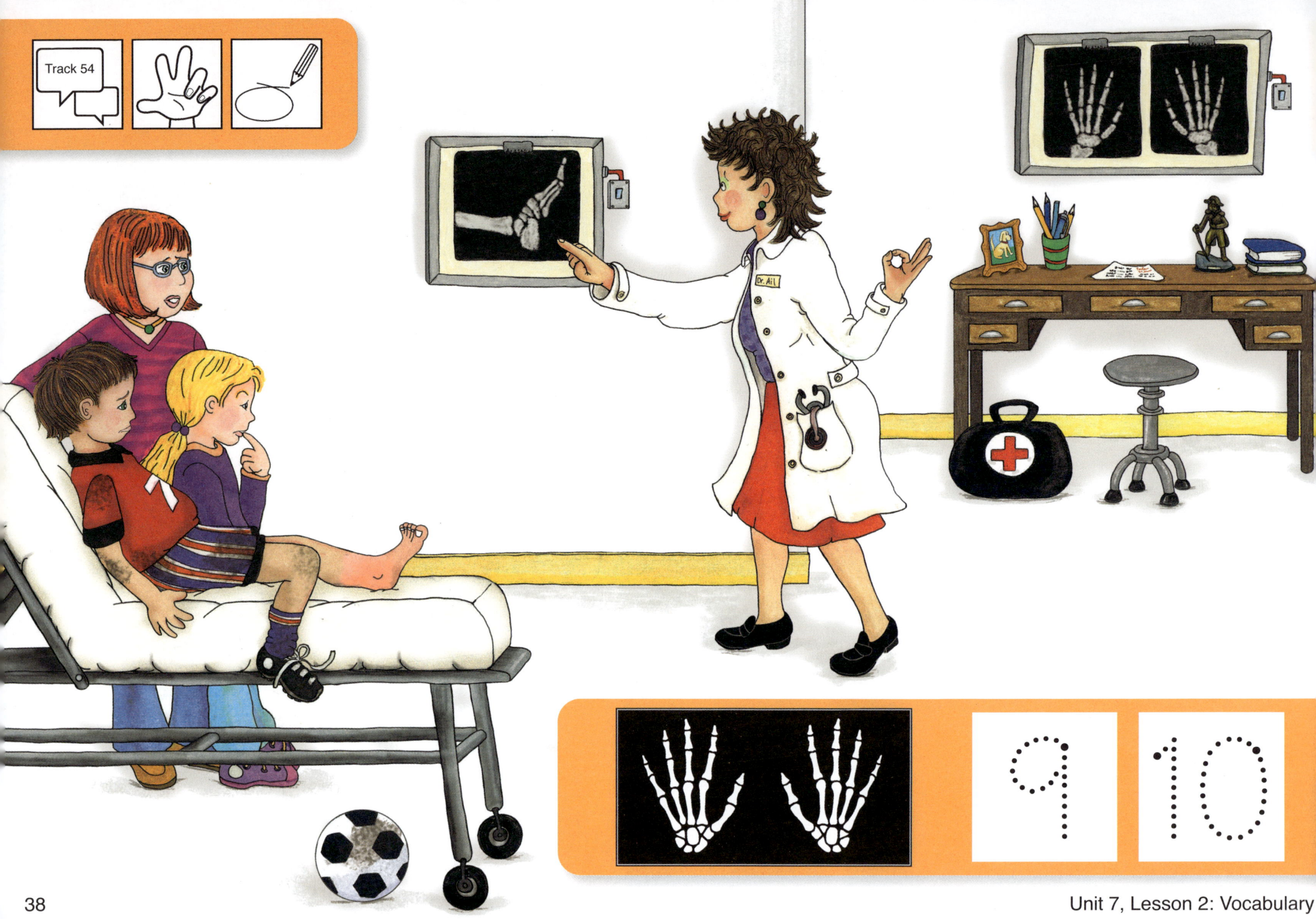

Track 55

Unit 7, Lesson 3: Story

A Party

Unit 8, Lesson 1: Vocabulary

Track 59

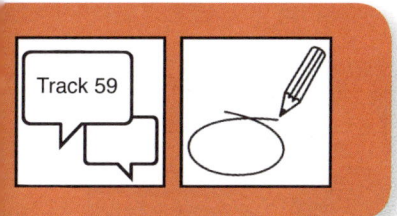

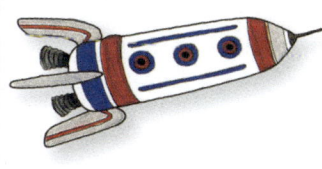

Unit 8, Lesson 2: Vocabulary

Track 60